D0990468

Understanding

Autism

Walk a Mile in Their Shoes

Beginners Guide to:

Diagnosis process, Creating Routines, Managing Sensory Difficulties, Surviving Meltdowns, And much more!

Speech and Language Therapist

Yasmin Akhtar

Acknowledgment

I would like to take this opportunity to say a HUGE thank you to all the amazing mums in my Facebook group, 'Kids delayed speech and language support group' who have been supporting me and my journey as a self-Publishing author. I know you are all busy, you have your jobs and your families to look after but you find time to read my books.

I just want you to know that I appreciate all your help and I will always try and make the group as valuable for you as your support is for me.

Thank you, you know who you are☺.

Table of Contents

A Gift For You!

Access your List of 10 Resources that will make life a little easier.

I have added links for each item with a little description.

(not affiliated) It is just for your ease. Some of the things on the list are...

- Special Toothbrush
- Weighted blanket which can help with anxiety
- Ear Defenders
- A set of Sensory fidget Toys and much more!

Click the link below to access the free list of Helpful Resources.

https://www.subscribepage.com/understanding-autism

Introduction

When you first hear the confirmation of an autistic diagnosis, the wave of emotions that hits you is bigger than your average tidal wave. Some parents are fearful of their child's future, others struggle to wonder how they will cope. You can see the mouths of doctors and specialists moving but no sound seems to be reaching you.

As parents, we gradually have to get used to our children falling over and hurting themselves, the terrible twos where no matter what you do the answer is no, worrying that they won't make friends at school or they will get bullied. We pass through one momentous stage only to start fearing the next. What nobody tells you in parenting classes is that the moment your child is born, you are constantly asking if you are doing the right thing or if something was your fault.

Now, as the parent of an autistic child, you know that all of these feelings are doubled, if not tripled. Your logical mind is already telling you that you did everything right and you aren't to blame but your heart tells you otherwise. You read stories from other parents of autistic children and half the time you feel reassured, the other half leaves you as a nervous wreck. It's hard to know where to start.

Whether your diagnosis is fairly new, or you are still trying to find the necessary information, 'research mode' can be like trying to find a needle in a haystack. The irony is, there is just so much information that it's difficult to find what you are looking for. There is a wonderful array of websites from experts and parents, and you will be able to find all sorts of great resources. But my aim is different.

Every child has the right to be treated differently, and this must be extended to autistic children. Every parent is different. An autistic diagnosis doesn't put you in a flock with all the other autistic parents, all moving in the same direction. As each person, family member and family dynamics are so different, the information for each case is going to be extensive— too extensive for one book.

At the same time, it's unlikely you have time to read an encyclopaedia on autism, despite the need and your determination. For these reasons, I am creating a series of short, easy to pick up books that will guide you on different areas of autism. Our first book will be dedicated to parents, understanding the diagnosis process, the changes that will have to be made and how to make sure you are getting the right amount of support.

You will be able to find simple changes that will make your routine easier and resources you can use. There will be ideas for home therapies and how you can use technology to your advantage. We will talk about some of my favourite books and even how to make mealtimes more enjoyable.

Most importantly, we will focus on seeing things from your child's point of view. How they might be in different social situations and what it's like for older autistic children to make friends. We will look at ways to handle frustration when things don't go their way as well as how you can cope with the variety of feelings that will rise up from loneliness to self-doubt.

There is also an essential topic that I want to cover that I feel isn't spoken about enough. The love, the joy, the successes, the amazing achievements you can accomplish together. There is no way we can sugar coat it, there will be difficult times ahead, however, there will also be some moments that you will be able to cherish forever. It is important to see your child as your child rather than a diagnosis. I have witnessed parents fraternizing over getting the ASD diagnosis that they forget to enjoy the little moments with their child, at the cost of their own mental health. I have spoken to so many mums who have said, they have become anxious and depressed thinking about what the future holds for their child.

Alternatively, some parents are in denial and do not even want to think about it even though the evidence is so stark. I can understand both sides of the argument. As a parent, you want the best for your child, and you are desperate for them to have a 'normal' life and get the best chances. It is heartbreaking when you know that your child may not have the same opportunities as their siblings or their peers.

As a speech and language therapist, I have worked with autistic children of all ages and across the entire autistic spectrum. Though not in my official job title, I love being there for families and carers in any way possible. It is thanks to these experiences as a therapist and a listening ear to family members, I have gathered years of experience that I would like to share. Respecting the fact that we are all different, I hope to provide enough advice about autism so that you have an arsenal of tips and tricks to explore.

Understanding Autism

Nobody can tell you what is right or wrong for your situation and I hope after reading this, you will have the tools and confidence to find out what is best for you and your child.

I know you want to gain an understanding of each and every aspect of autism. Further books will focus on speech and language, therapies, school and education, and any other ideas you would like advice on. Still, I wanted this first book to be support for parents as I am a firm believer that happy, healthy parents raise happy, healthy children. Making sure that you are mentally and physically in the right place is the best start for raising your little one.

On that note, let's begin with a better understanding of what autism is.

Chapter 1: Understanding Autism— The Whole 9 Yards!

The last thing I want to do is assume that some readers are complete novices on the topic of autism. Many of you will already have an understanding of what autism is and the autism spectrum. That being said, I am committed to providing the necessary information for every type of reader. Some parents may have that initial feeling that something isn't quite right and aren't too sure where to begin.

If you are a few steps ahead, think of this as your favourite film— you've seen it many times, but you wouldn't mind watching it again to refresh your memory and maybe even spot some new things.

Using the Correct Terms

I'm hoping that I don't alienate any reader so early on in the book, but I have trouble calling autism a disability. The National Autistic Society classes autism as a "lifelong developmental disability". My problem with the term disability is that many autistic children go on to lead very normal lives. They have a job, a car, relationships, etc. I have spoken to autistic adults who would not consider themselves to be disabled.

The overall preferred term is Autism Spectrum

Understanding Autism

Conditions (ASC). This term is far more collective and can encompass all types of autism conditions:

Autistic Spectrum Disorder- this is what you would consider as the traditional type of autism. Symptoms often present with speech and language delays, struggles with social interactions and what others would see as unusual behaviours or 'quirks. It is common to also experience intellectual challenges however not all children with ASD have issues with language or intellect.

Pervasive Development Disorder- because we are still learning more and more about autism, there are some people who show certain symptoms but not all. This can also be referred to as PDD-NOS (not otherwise specified) or atypical autism.

The reason we use the word spectrum is that autism can affect different people in different ways. The condition can be very mild or severe. One child may display strong symptoms with social interactions and the next have more difficulties with repetitive behaviours.

For the purpose of this book, we will refer to the preferred term, autism spectrum disorder or ASD.

Yasmin Akhtar

Difficulties that Come with Autism

As a therapist, the one thing I try to remind parents is not to start panicking. I have seen a few different things happen in the early days and to an extent, these events have their own spectrum. There are parents who find it difficult to accept that their child has difficulties and there are others who become so overwhelmed they are convinced each of the following applies to their child. My advice here isn't to start diagnosing your child. Instead, read the information from an outsider's perspective so that you can fully grasp what ASD could feel like.

1. Communication

Difficulties in communication can be verbal and/or non-verbal. Some children will have delays in speech or have very limited to no speech. They might need longer to understand what is being said and take longer to reply to your questions. All children go through learning and playful phases of repeating things. If your child is only repeating words after you but they do not have any words of their own, this is what we call echolalia. Your child is echoing what you are saying. They will be able to repeat your words clearly but that does not mean they have understood what you have said. For example, you might say to your child, 'shall we go out', your child will repeat, "shall we go out", without understanding what the words mean. Some children can do this while they are learning new vocabulary, however, if it's extreme enough to cause you concern, it could be a sign of ASD.

Children with ASD have difficulties with 'inferencing' meaning, from what is said or implied, therefore it is difficult for them to understand sarcasm. ASD children will mostly take your words very literally. If you tell your autistic child to "get a wiggle on", they could start wriggling instead of hurrying up. It's also true that autistic children can learn to understand idioms and be taught to recognize them. Another big change you might notice is speech regression. You may notice that your little one who was saying a few single words and even starting to put 2 words together, is no longer saying any words. This regression is another 'red flag' for ASD.

2. Social Interaction

This is linked to social communication skills, for example, making eye contact with the person who is talking to you, or being able to take turns in a simple game which in turn will develop your skills to take turns during a conversation with others. This also includes being able to 'read' how others are feeling, so being able to read body language, facial expressions etc. Again, you might be saying to yourself that this is another learning stage for younger children as nobody is born with the ability to recognize emotions.

I am not saying that all children who can't take turns or don't make appropriate eye contact when talking to adults will be diagnosed with ASD, however, it is really important to seek help if you have concerns. You might notice that it is hard for your child to create friendships, perhaps because they come across as insensitive or because they have problems expressing emotions and understanding other people's points of view. It might be that they don't want to play with friends or share certain toys. It might also be their unusual behaviours that other children find hard to get past. They may not understand 'personal space' and get too close or step over toys or walk through a game their peers were playing on the floor and enjoying.

One thing that many parents find incredibly hard is when their child struggles to cope with physical contact, even hugs and kisses. The limited or lack of eye contact might be difficult for both parents and peers, as well as the difficulties with adult-led activities, regardless of the surrounding. Sometimes, autistic children are far more comfortable following their own agenda.

3. Routine and Repetition

As new parents, the word routine is often drilled into our heads. Routine is great but ASD children can become highly anxious when their routine is broken. This could be a small change like driving instead of taking the bus or something larger like holidays from school. The act of doing something repetitively can be very soothing for ASD children and in some cases, even enjoyable for them. The range of actions that can be repeated is vast. It could be from tapping, rocking, or pacing, as just a few examples.

4. The Sensitive Child

Parents of ASD children have to be very careful of sensory overloads. Take a step back and think about the extent of your senses. Most of us will agree that things like fingernails on a blackboard go right through us. For ASD children, the same feelings can occur from any type of sound, smell, touch, taste or even particular colours and temperatures. These sensory overloads may not just upset them but can also cause them pain. They may also experience under-sensitivity to certain things.

5. Dealing with Anxiety and Meltdowns

I know what you're thinking! Your 2-year-old had a complete meltdown yesterday because you gave them orange carrots instead of blue. We are used to temper tantrums and they normally resolve themselves once the child has calmed down. How can you tell the difference? Instincts will likely kick in. When a child has a temper tantrum, we have to do all we can to stop ourselves from becoming angrier because the cause is almost laughable (blue carrots, not wanting to get dressed, taking the cat to the bath, etc.). Because meltdowns are caused by extreme anxiety due to the physical environment or psychological causes, it is much harder for you to provide comfort.

6. A Fascination with Hobbies

ASD children can become engrossed with a particular interest or hobby. It may begin at a surprisingly young age but stick with them for their entire childhood and even as adults. To an extent, this is great because it can help them focus, a skill that is transferable academically, on something that makes them happy. It may become problematic when the children have to concentrate on other tasks.

Looking at the positive side or managing this obsession with hobbies, we can use this to "bargain' with the child to carry out the necessary learning in school. I have seen a teacher give 5 cards to a child at the beginning of the school day. Every time the child talks about their particular subject of interest with an adult or peer, they have to give one card back to the teacher. The teacher then reminds them 'remember you have only 4 cards left now' etc. When all the cards have gone, the child will be discouraged to talk about the hobby, so over time, the child will learn to talk about their hobby more sparingly. As the child gets older, the number of cards can be reduced so they will likely be forced to focus and complete the schoolwork.

I personally like to use a 2-minute 'timer'. I ask the child, what they would like to do, tell me about their hobby at the beginning or end of the clinic session. I find that the child can then concentrate better on the assessment or therapy task.

Having the opportunity to talk about what makes them happy but also not being consumed by talking about the hobby, especially in an educational setting is important.

In the next chapter, we will look at more specific symptoms that you might be concerned about as a parent. For now, we have touched on a very general overview of what autism and ASD is.

A History Lesson in ASD— How Far We Have Come!

The history of autism doesn't necessarily relate to your situation now, but I find it motivating. 100 odd years may sound like a long time but the advances in this century have been outstanding, and more so in recent years. The reason I like to look back at history is that it shows us just how far we have come.

Before the 1980s, there were very few studies on autism. The word autism was first used by Eugen Bleuler in 1908 and it was used to describe people who were severely withdrawn schizophrenics.

Almost 4 decades later, the focus was more on children. Child psychiatrist Leo Kanner noticed social interaction difficulties in 11 children. These difficulties included echolalia, sensitivity to stimuli, in particular sound, and challenges with changes in the routine and unplanned activities. He also noticed that the children had good memories and intellectual potential. A year later, Hans Asperger carried out his own study with similar results. His group, however, didn't display echolalia but were lacking in fine motor skills.

One theory that we can thankfully look back on and laugh at is Bruno Bettelheim's theory that autism in children was caused by the coldness of their mothers. Fortunately, Bernard Rimland, psychologist, and parent of an autistic child, jumped to the defence of his wife. He turned the attention to neurology and neural therapy.

Even in the 70s, autism was still seen as a psychotic issue among children. Sadly, this association with autism and mental retardation still exists as a misconception for some people today.

When Hans Asperger's work was translated into English in the 80s, people's understanding began to change and so did the level of research. More and more specialists were emphasizing that parents were not the cause of autism but that it was due to neurological, metabolic, or chromosomal disturbances.

The First Autistic Diagnosis

Donald Triplett was born in 1933. After his parents noticed their son's difficulties in social situations as well as a fixation on specific objects and an incredible memory, they agreed that they couldn't cope with his delays in development and, as considered normal in 'those days' they committed him to an institution in 1937. He was taken back out a year later and then actually became one of the children in Leo Kanner's study.

What I love about Donald Triplett was that he went to high school, earned his degree in French, and worked in the family bank. He learnt how to drive and enjoyed travelling. He wasn't cured and some of his symptoms remained present all through his adult life, but he lived and still lives what many would consider a normal life.

Yasmin Akhtar

Autism Today

Knowing how much has been achieved brings hope with regards to the future and the changes that parents, and specialists can make. One of the greatest changes that we have to make is acceptance. Naturally, I haven't personally spoken to Triplett, but his books give a general feeling of acceptance from his high school friends to his community where he lives today.

Another area that needs improvement is the definition of autism. We briefly looked at the range of symptoms and to say that they are broad is an understatement. Some autistic people may need around the clock support, others may thrive in a world that doesn't fear or misunderstand ASD. It doesn't seem right to diagnose these extremes under the same disorder, despite the word spectrum.

In the UK, there are approximately 700,000 people with autism. One in every hundred UK children are on the autistic spectrum. In the USA, the CDC stated that around 1 in 54 8-year-olds had ASD in 2016 and that it was 4.3 times more likely to occur in boys. ASD can be found in all races and ethnic groups.

Some fear an autism epidemic due to the rising number of cases. This is certainly not the case. What has happened is that as we get better at understanding ASD, we get better and correctly diagnosing children and even adults. This diagnosis, however, has to come from a professional as the risks of over and under-diagnosis is still a real thing.

What is unbelievable are those who are labelling autism as the 'fashionable disability'. Even more unbelievable is, for example, the Korean's excitement and their high ASD numbers. Even as I write this, I feel the fear of self-diagnoses and those people who label a child as autistic as an explanation for their unusual behaviours. For this reason, our next chapter will cover the exact process of a correct and professional ASD diagnosis.

Chapter 2: The Diagnosis Process— Who Is Involved?

At this point, you might be 100% convinced that your child is on the autistic spectrum or you may just have a feeling. The one thing all parents have in common is a wonderful natural instinct that should be followed. If you have read chapter 1 and some things are ringing a bell, it might be time to start looking for professional help.

At this stage, I have to reiterate the complexities of an autistic diagnosis and specifically the word 'normal'. Because the spectrum is so broad, it can be difficult to know what falls under the term 'normal' and what is considered a cause for concern. From here on in I will stop using normal inside apostrophes and please understand that when I use this word it refers to what is considered standard for a child's development at a particular age. It is normal for children to start saying their first words between 10 and fifteen months. Bilingual children are normal, but they may not speak their first words in the normal age range.

So, we have established that your child is normal but there are some things that are worrying you, keeping you up at night, or even making you slightly overprotective of your child. What do you do next?

In some cases, it is worth talking to friends and family members about your concerns. This is still not an official diagnosis, but it does help to reassure you on whether your worries are genuine or if you are worrying yourself about a potential symptom that all children may go through.

For example, I remember talking to one mum who had read that continuously taking socks off could be a symptom of autism. To a certain degree, this is true, but not restricted to socks. Some autistic children want to remove clothes because a particular item makes them feel uncomfortable. After a long day, you want to take your shoes off because it brings such a sense of relief. That is not out of the ordinary. As autistic children feel things in a different way, even the sensation of socks can upset them. However, after this mum was able to talk about her concerns, she began to realise that this was more likely to be a phase than a symptom. By talking to other parents, you may learn that other non-autistic children have these quirks. It's only when you combine them with other symptoms that autism becomes a greater possibility.

The First Steps to an ASD Diagnosis

Different countries may have their own specific procedure, that being said, the general process is the same. We will follow the ASD diagnosis for the UK.

Yasmin Akhtar

The first two years especially are filled with medical appointments for vaccinations, height and weight, and general check-ups.

Most concerns about your child's speech and language development should be raised with your Health Visitor first. You can either wait until you have your child's 2-year check-up and then discuss your concerns with the health visitor, and they will be able to offer reassurance or tell you that your concerns are valid, and they can make a referral to your local speech and language therapy service. They can also refer your child to community paediatrics for a full assessment too if they are concerned about your child's delayed speech and language development and social communication difficulties. If the health visitor is not sure, they may only refer you for speech therapy first then your speech therapist can refer you to Paediatrician if required.

If I can make one suggestion, when you have your appointment with your GP or your Health Visitor, try not to be vague about your concerns. It makes the appointment much easier if you have a list of things that you are worried about. In some areas, you will be able to refer your child to speech therapy directly.

If your child has started attending nursery, the nursery will raise concerns if they notice any unusual traits in your child. You can always talk to nursery staff or school special educational needs coordinator

(SENDCo) about your concerns, and they should be able to support you. They will also suggest a referral to speech therapy with your consent of course.

The outcome of assessment by the GP, health visitor or/and a speech therapist will determine whether or not your child requires further assessment to determine a diagnosis of ASD.

What Does An ASD Assessment Entail- What You Need To Know

An ASD assessment will be carried out by the autism specialist team. The next logical question would be, who is in the autism specialist team? Don't start to panic and the list of potential assessors. Big official titles don't make big scary people! As one of those on the following list, I promise we are dedicated to being approachable (smiley face emoji). Aside from Speech and Language Therapists, the assessment team may include:

- A developmental paediatrician
- A psychologist
- A child psychiatrist
- An autism trained specialist teacher
- A play therapist

Yasmin Akhtar

It's perfectly normal for a parent to hear these titles and start to panic. Please don't! Know that it takes a multidisciplinary team to accurately diagnose ASD. After your initial meeting with a paediatrician, the paediatrician will then request reports from all the professionals involved with your child's care, for example, health visitor, speech and language therapist and school SENCo. After talking through your concerns, and looking at all the reports, if all the professionals have reported concerns, your child will be referred to a Joint Assessment Communication Clinic (jacc). Sadly, there is often a long waiting list for this. This assessment involves two of the professionals mentioned above and the remaining professionals observing from a different room. As the parent, you will be in the room with your child. It's not a scary experience for the child. The environment is very much play-based, and the professionals will observe how your child plays and interacts.

Once the session is over the professionals meet to discuss what they have observed, and they will also look at the reports together and compare the results. They will complete the necessary documents from notes from their observations on the day and the reports and then decide if the autism criteria have been met. It might not be a simple yes or no diagnosis. If the professionals feel that only some criteria are met, they might request a new assessment in 6 months.

ASD Diagnostic Tools—How The Diagnosis Is Given

Within the ASD assessment, professionals can use different tools or structures to determine a diagnosis. We will take a closer look at three so that you are more familiar with certain terms you may hear or read.

DISCO- Diagnostic Interview for Social and Communication Disorders

A DISCO assessment is a semi-structured interview that finds out great detail about someone's developmental skills and their behaviour. It can be used for any age and any level of ability although as it is not play-based, it is often reserved for older children and adults. It is extremely useful because it encompasses challenges and behaviours that aren't only on the autism spectrum.

Professionals carrying out a DISCO assessment will focus on gathering the person's history in as much depth as possible, whether that's from the person themselves or from someone who has known them since birth. Because the interview isn't only concerned with autism, it may also provide insight into conditions that are associated with ASD like dyspraxia or ADHD.

Yasmin Akhtar

ADOS- Autism Diagnostic Observation Schedule

Since its beginnings in 2000, the ADOS is now used in 15 different languages around the world. It's another semi-structured assessment and a standard diagnostic tool for schools and medical professionals. Because it is a standardized tool, it can help to reduce the differences in opinion among professionals. ADOS doesn't look at the history of a person. Instead, it looks at the current behaviour and skills of a person.

The assessment uses 4 modules, and it may involve one or various modules. The modules contain different, and the most appropriate assessments for a particular age or level. Each module lasts approximately 40 minutes, and the person is given a score of zero to three, zero considered as normal behaviour and three as abnormal behaviour. If a person goes through more than one module, the average is calculated.

ADI-R- Autism Diagnostic Interview-Revised

The Autism Diagnostic Interview has been used for years. It is a semi-structured comprehensive interview. Since being revised, it has become one of the more formal diagnosis tools as well as helping in treatment and educational planning. It combines a person's developmental history as current behaviour

24

and skills and is suitable for all ages as long as the person has a mental age of above 2 years old.

There are 93 items in the assessment covering language and communication, reciprocal social interactions and restricted, repetitive, and stereotyped behaviours and interests. These three areas are then further separated into 8 sub-sections:

1. Family, education, and medical history

2. Overview of behaviour

3. Early development and milestones

4. The acquisition of language, loss of language or other skills

5. Current language and communication level

6. Social development and play

7. Interests and behaviour

8. Relevant behaviours- aggressiveness, self-injury, etc.

Again, these tools won't be used to complete an ASD diagnosis. They will be used as a part of the assessment and can only be carried out by specialists of that particular tool.

Yasmin Akhtar

Can You Disagree With a Diagnosis?

A complete report is going to have an awful lot of detail and it is understandable if you don't understand all of it. Like legal contracts and other industry-specific reports, ASD reports contain a lot of medical terminologies. Before you rush to contest a diagnosis, don't be afraid to ask any questions regarding the results. I also think it is a good idea to take a day or two so that you can process and let the information sink in.

If you don't agree with the diagnosis, you can go back to your GP or paediatrician who can refer you for a second opinion. Just be prepared for the same diagnosis with a second opinion.

Alternatively, you might want to contact one of the ASD associations:

Autism Speaks- **International**

The National Autistic Society- **UK**

NHS- **UK**

The Autism Society- **USA**

Autism Connect- **Australia**

Late Diagnosis— How Late Is Late?

Bearing in mind that a child is typically diagnosed with autism around the age of 3. It might feel strange to hear the words 'late autism diagnosis' when your child is just 6 or 7. A late diagnosis is considered for older children and teenagers. Also, remember that the word late doesn't mean you have done anything wrong or haven't taken action in time.

When a person doesn't display language or delayed skill symptoms, it might not be until primary school when behavioural symptoms begin to present. In other cases, this could occur in secondary school. It is at these crucial moments when children's social skills really start to develop as they face the challenges of making new friends.

For a late autism diagnosis, your paediatrician will ask the school and the speech and language therapist for a detailed report about your child's learning and social communication skills. The paediatrician will then refer your child to the Joint Assessment Communication Clinic (jacc) in order to reach a diagnosis. It is again a long process, and no diagnosis is made lightly. Still, not every parent will agree, and, in this case, they can ask for a referral after a period of time.

The most important thing that I cannot emphasize enough is that a diagnosis in older children and teenagers is not about putting a label on them or putting them in a category. Your child will be no different if an ASD diagnosis is confirmed. It is often harder in older children because the struggles become more apparent. No parent wants to see their child have difficulties making friends. But the last thing your child needs, especially a teenager, is your pity.

Receiving a late autism diagnosis is great because you can now start focusing on your child's strengths and where they excel. You can also find more help so that you are better able to support and guide them. This is the only thing that should change with a late autism diagnosis.

Can Adults Get an ASD Diagnosis?

Essentially, this book is aimed at parents with children. However, that's not to say there might be some parents who have adult children, and they might have concerns. For this reason, we will take a quick look at autism in adults.

If you think that the first autism diagnosis was in 1935 but then it wasn't until the 80s that research really began to take off, there is a whole generation or two that could be walking around undiagnosed. The old man down the road who has always been considered "a bit slow" may well be on the autism spectrum but never been tested, as may granny who we always thought was just cold and didn't like us.

I have to reiterate that you can't go through your entire list of adult family and friends and start assuming they are all on the spectrum. It's just to highlight that while we are getting much better at early diagnosis, we shouldn't forget the adults that could also lead a more fulfilling life with the correct diagnosis. Here are some of the signs that may indicate autism in adults:

- Difficulty taking turns in conversations. They may interrupt or dominant conversations with what is on their mind. It can be a challenge for them to see things from other people's perspectives.

- Hyper focus on a hobby or interest, which is apparent in conversations.

- Taking things literally, whether that is idioms or not being able to detect sarcasm. They may also misinterpret language and even social situations.

- Abnormal eye contact and /or body language, which makes it hard for them to be a part of social circles. They may come across as antisocial as they don't seem to be motivated to interact with others.

Yasmin Akhtar

- It is often difficult for autistic adults to adapt their behaviour to match the needs of the social situation.

- They prefer to stick to very strict routines and can become anxious, irritated, or upset when this routine is broken.

- Some autistic adults might not be able to carry out everyday tasks, particularly if they are extremely sensitive to sounds, light, smells, etc.

- They may avoid any or certain forms of physical contact. On the other hand, they might get too close to others. Both will make social situations more challenging.

As with late diagnosis, an autism diagnosis for adults isn't going to change anything. It just means that there is more support available. If you think you might be on the autism spectrum or you are worried about another adult, in some areas of the UK, you can refer yourself for an autism assessment, however, the best place to start might be your GP so that the correct, professional assessment process can begin.

A Little Bit About The Girls and Boys— The Gender Differences

With a significantly higher ratio of male to female ASD diagnosis, many scientists have wondered what the reason behind this is. At present, there is no evidence to support the difference as being genetic and so the explanation so far lies in the diagnosis.

By nature, and generally speaking, girls and women are quieter and often more reserved. This has become known as camouflaging. Essentially, girls are better at hiding the symptoms of ASD and therefore making it harder to diagnose. Females may be better at suppressing their inappropriate behaviours in social situations and they may even be better at forcing certain behaviours like making eye contact or facial expressions that match the tone of a conversation or circumstances.

This is another reason why it is crucial to get a professional diagnosis because specialists are trained to pick up on certain behaviours that might be gender specific.

The main aim I had with this chapter was to remove the fear of the diagnostic process. Regardless of age, gender, skills and behaviour, a diagnosis should be seen as a relief rather than a label. When you wake up on your 40th birthday, technically you are a year older, but has anything changed overnight? A

Yasmin Akhtar

diagnosis is the first step to getting the right help. This help comes in all shapes and sizes from your family to your child's school and your speech therapist. There is also an awful lot that you can do at home that can support your autistic child, help them to flourish, and take some of the pressure off you as a parent. We will cover this topic in the next chapter.

Chapter 3: Lifestyle Changes You Will Need to Make

In no way am I comparing myself to an autistic child but even adults have moments when things get too much for them. Think back to that time at work when you were bombarded with new information, requests, to-do lists that only seem to grow. I have a huge issue with 2 lots of music or sounds at the same time. I have a friend who gets physically sick at the smell of fish. We all have things that we find hard to cope with. Now let's multiply that by 10 or 100 or even a thousand— oh yes, and imagine you are a child.

You may have recently received an autism diagnosis or be nervously waiting, perhaps you have been trying various strategies and not seeing the results you were hoping for. The great news is that there are numerous things you can do that may only seem small but can make an exponential difference to your child's life.

Sensory Subject— Understanding and Making the Changes

When considering sensory information, we must go beyond our traditional view of the 5 senses and look at anything that may cause an information overload

Yasmin Akhtar

for your autistic child. In each sense, your child could show hypersensitivity (an extreme reaction) or hyposensitivity (a less than usual response) Before we look at the changes you could make, here are some of the factors that may be too much for your little one.

Sight

If a child is under sensitive, they may have a poor perception of depth. This makes them appear as if they are clumsy. Things may seem darker than they actually are. On the contrary, oversensitivity causes things to appear brighter, which is why they may struggle to fall asleep.

Sound

Under sensitivity can present as liking loud noises. They might not be able to hear certain sounds, or they may not be able to hear with both ears. Children who are oversensitive to sounds often have trouble concentrating. It can be hard for them to ignore background sound or sounds may seem louder than they are.

Smell

Certain things may have no smell, or they might be overwhelmingly strong. For those who are oversensitive to smell, you might notice an extreme reaction to particular cleaning products, air fresheners or perfumes.

Taste

We will talk more about diet in the next section but under sensitivity might mean that your child is keen on spicy food. Pica is a condition where people eat inedible things, stones, paper, or plastic. You may have already noticed your child refusing to eat particular colours or textures.

Touch

There is a wide range for both over and under sensitivity. If your child is under sensitive to touch, it might be something small like holding your hand too tightly or preferring heavy blankets and bedding. Others may have a high pain threshold, and some might turn to self-harm such as banging their head on the floor or hitting their head with their hands. Oversensitivity is when children don't like to be touched. As heart-breaking as this is for you as a parent, it's important to remember that this is not a sign that your child doesn't love you. It could be that physical contact causes them pain. Textures may also cause issues, particularly around the hands and feet. Even brushing their hair could be too much for them so going to the hairdressers for a haircut would be out of the question.

Balance

A common symptom of autism is the need for constant movement such as rocking or swinging. This is a sign of under sensitivity to balance. Children who are oversensitive are prone to car sickness and might find psychical activities more challenging, more so when their feet aren't touching the ground.

Body Awareness

Another thing that we would take for granted is our body awareness or our perception of our bodies within a room. It is hard to imagine not being aware of how your arms and legs move in relation to the space that you have. If a child is under sensitive, they may not be aware of someone else's personal space, maybe even stand too close. They may knock into people or objects around the home. Typically, oversensitivity is related to challenges with fine motor skills.

What Is Synaesthesia?

It's a fascinating yet rare condition and not limited to autism. Synaesthesia is a condition where one sense causes a reaction in another. So, some people might be able to hear colours, or they might literally see sounds. While it sounds like a kind of superpower, it can be incredibly perplexing for an autistic child. If you want to disconnect for 40 minutes and you like crime thrillers, you could watch Episode 9, Season 8 of Criminal Minds. No— your child is not destined to become a serial killer, but I felt that the episode highlighted the difficulties well.

How You Can Help

I am a huge fan of getting down and dirty at this stage. The best way to try and understand the extent of what your autistic child is experiencing is to test your own senses. If this means running your hands over a Scotch Brite/brillo pad, wearing sunglasses in your house for a day or turning the TV down so you can barely hear it, explore your own environment, and see exactly what is upsetting your child's senses and where this is occurring. This is a great way to help you become more aware of what they are experiencing.

Here are some ideas regarding the changes you can make:

- Look at changing light bulbs to ones that aren't so bright or if need be, provide extra lighting in parts of the room that are darker. Blackout curtains can help in the bedroom.

- Create a work/play station that suits their sensory needs.

- Create flashcards or other visual materials that can help provide verbal information for those who struggle with under sensitivity to light.

- Find ways to reduce external sounds that might upset or distract your child. Closing doors and windows might help, as could a set of headphones.

- Make your home as fragrance-free as possible, pay special attention to shampoos and fabric softeners and other cleaning products.

- Have a box of different materials that your child can play with-known as a multi-sensory box. You can also include different toys that light up or have music. Don't force the issue but have some of their favourite things they like to touch as well as new things that they can gradually begin exploring.

- Cut labels out of clothes and let your child choose the clothes they would like to wear; it will help them feel more comfortable.

- Encourage your child to explore the swings and see-saw at the park to develop their balance. Break down sports and physical activities into smaller tasks so that it is easier for them to master their skills.

- Teach your child the one arm's length rule so that they learn to understand personal space.

- Have fine motor activities in your play box, we will talk more about this in Chapter 5.

As we know that autistic children are quite set in their routine, try not to make too many changes at once. Although they are all relatively small changes, you don't want to have the opposite effect and cause more anxiety for them. Changing the furniture is great to make a room easier for them to move around, but if you then change the lighting and their toy box on the same day, it may feel like more information overload.

ASD Diet and Eating Habits

I remember my mum and gran having a good old moan about what a fussy eater I was as a child. Between the two of them, they came up with some innovative ideas to ensure I was eating a balanced diet, some of which I hope will inspire you.

The one thing I must add here is that you should never try to force your child to eat food they don't like, whether they are autistic or not. I have never got over my fear of baked beans after my dad told me I wasn't to leave the table until they were all gone. I actually had a stomach bug and my mum pretty much had to cope with me being sick all night. Forcing children to eat things they don't like causes them to associate that with bad experiences.

Yasmin Akhtar

It's even more important not to force an autistic child to eat foods they don't like. Unlike me, they aren't fussy eaters, and they are not intent on creating more work for you. Have you ever had sensitive teeth? Remember the pain when you ate ice cream? Try to imagine the level of pain your child could feel when they eat a banana or rice? What about if you felt the same level of anxiety when eating pizza as you did giving a presentation to 100 strangers? This isn't about comparing; it's about trying to see things from your child's perspective so that you are better able to find the best solutions and still ensure they are eating a balanced diet.

Aside from dietary issues related to smells, tastes and textures, there are other things that might worry you about your child's eating habits.

- They might not be eating enough- if your child has a hard time concentrating, this may apply to mealtimes too. It is recommended that children have 20 minutes to eat a meal, for an autistic child, even if it's their favourite meal, 20 minutes is a long time.

- Medication may affect appetite- there are certain medications that can reduce a child's appetite. If you are already struggling with mealtimes, this can make things worse.

- A preference for particular foods- many notice that their children prefer starchy foods over fruit and vegetables. Some will refuse to eat anything that isn't bland in colour. This may be due to their sensitivity to colour.

- Meltdowns at the table- when all seems to be going well, a seemingly small disruption could cause your child to have a meltdown, get upset, or anxious. You may find it hard to bring the focus back to the meal.

The first thing that you need to do is to make sure all meals have their routine. Keep to the same time and even the same seat at the table. They should be having three meals plus a mid-morning and mid-afternoon snack, again, as part of a routine. Although you might be worried about them not eating enough but offering food in between snacks could cause them not to eat during their scheduled meals.

When it comes to introducing a new food, you might want to start by taking your child shopping with you. Take some time to look around at the fruits and vegetables and see if they pick out something they want to try. When you introduce a new food, don't try hiding it in something else— they will end up finding the piece of food and then you might have a tantrum on your hands! Put it on a smaller plate next to their meal. It might sound silly but keep the piece of new food small, even as small as one single pea or green bean. You could even try planting some vegetables or fruit to spark more of an interest.

If your child is partial to purees, you might be able to get away with hiding the good foods within the puree so try to take advantage of this. Again, it has to be done very gradually so that they don't notice slight changes in colour or taste. For example, small amounts of cauliflower or aubergine/eggplant won't change the colour of mashed potato and they are relatively flavourless, but they do get some added nutrients into their diet. The same can be done with smoothies or any other type of blended foods they like. Bolognese and soups are also good for adding vegetables or seeds, always gradually.

Take things out of boxes and packages. This will prevent children from becoming attached to certain brands. It is quite frustrating to find a food your child likes and then for them not to eat it because it's in the wrong colour box.

It's a messy task but try to have some baking sessions with your children. It's great fun and you can explore different textures and tastes while you are cooking— if they want to. Seeing the end result of something they made may also make them more willing to try it.

If you are concerned, you should see a nutritionist and if possible, one with experience with autistic children. Your team of specialists will likely be able to recommend one.

Coping With Strict Routines

We have already touched on the need for routine throughout the first chapters. As with food. It's not about having a tantrum because they aren't doing what they want, or they don't want to do a certain activity. Autistic children are comforted by routine, plans, and knowing what is going to happen in their day.

Every family will have their own general routine in terms of school, work, mealtimes, and weekend activities. The issues we often have are when things come up that you can't help. Maybe someone in the family is sick and you aren't around as much. You might need to call on a friend or sitter if you have to go to work for an emergency. Having a routine is a marvellous thing— until it is broken. These things will come up in life and there is little you can do about it. Be careful not to put your life on hold for fear of upsetting the balance. In these situations, it's a good idea to make sure that the person you call on to look after your little one is someone that they feel comfortable with and someone who knows your child well so that their routine is disrupted as little as possible. It's also better if they can come to your house rather than taking your child to theirs.

Yasmin Akhtar

That being said. It is hardly imaginable that you are going to spend the foreseeable years glued to your routine and emergencies. You will want to plan days out and even holidays. If you have watched your child struggle with changes in a routine, you are probably thinking that the sheer thought of a holiday is too much. Any change to the routine should be planned and frequently discussed with your child. You should have a calendar and mark the date, check the calendar every day so you are counting down the days together. Look for pictures of your planned activity, print them out and look at them together. You can also read stories about it. Take advantage of their hyper focus on interests and hobbies. If your child loves a certain animal, see if there is a zoo with that animal.

When doing things that aren't out of your child's routine, try to stick to certain parts of your child's routine. One good thing to stick to is the same mealtimes and even taking their plates, cups, and cutlery if need be. Let them choose their favourite clothes for the day or help you choose clothes to pack. Include any toys, blankets, all of the things that you know soothe them when things become too much.

Safety, Safety, Safety

You have probably already taken steps to 'baby-proof your home. You have put all of the hazardous

44

products well out of reach, the electric sockets have plastic coverings, and you have various baby/stair. You may have rearranged your furniture so that the layout is safer, added slip-resistant mats to the bath and so on. Let's take a couple of minutes to look at ways to make your home a safer environment for your child.

- Organize their toys in plastic boxes and in places where they can see them but can't necessarily reach them. You can also use labels and visual cues. You may have a pantry or garden shed that you can put a stop sign on, or cupboards and drawers that they shouldn't be in.

- Pay closer attention to things that can be put in mouths. All children go through a phase of putting things in their mouths but because it is not a phase for autistic children, you need to be more conscious of keeping these things out of reach.

- Attach plates and cutlery to the table. I love this trick. Because mealtimes are prime time for meltdowns and potentially aggressive behaviour, it's not uncommon for autistic children to throw whatever is closest to them. Not nice for the sibling or parent that is sitting next to them. You can attach cutlery to a piece of string (think the pen in the bank!) and use Velcro for plates and cups.

- Place additional locks on windows. For older children who bang on glass, it might be worth replacing the glass with Plexiglas.

- Fire safety is going to be a challenge, especially if loud sounds upset your child. Still, it can't be ignored. Books and videos are good ways to explain fire safety to an autistic child. If you can introduce them to videos with fire alarms, you can introduce them to the sound of an alarm without the intensity of a real fire alarm. Along with fire safety, there are various other situations that can cause anxiety; however, the anxiety can be reduced with rehearsal. These are called social stories and can be about anything from going on holiday to having a baby brother or sister. Therapists may provide some or you can write your own.

- Use locks and alarms. As your child gets older, they might like to explore the outside world more. Windows and locks need to have the right types of locks so that children and even teens can't get out, but you can still open quickly in case of an emergency.

- If your child does start wandering off, consider contacting your local police and/or fire department. ASD identification is such a good idea, however, not every child will like the feel of bracelets or necklaces. You can teach your child to carry and show an ASD identification card or use iron-on labels for clothes.

When it comes to safety, it is always better to be safe than sorry.

Be Careful Who You Listen To— The Supplement Spectrum

As I mentioned in the introduction, there is a wealth of information online today and this truly is fantastic. We love it. We love how parents are able to share their stories and what works for them. Because new studies pop up all the time, more often than not, parents who share ideas on Autism forums are able to spread the word about the latest studies. One area, in particular, is the use of supplements to help ease the symptoms of autism. Some examples I have heard of include:

- Vitamin D
- Oxytocin
- Omega-3 and fish oil
- Sulforaphane
- Methyl Vitamin B-12

- Probiotics

I am certainly not saying that you shouldn't try these supplements but notice that I am not going to go into their details either. My only concern is that supplements are made artificially to mimic how natural nutrients act in our bodies. I would urge you to check with your paediatrician or nutritionist before starting your child on any supplements and especially if they are already on other medications.

If your specialist says there is no harm in trying, then great. It takes time to see the results of therapies and so you may feel like supplements can offer some additional relief and faster. As long as no harm is being done, even the placebo effect can provide some temporary relief.

OK, so for little changes I know that was a long chapter. If you are feeling like there is a lot to do, remember that for the sake of your child, you can't do it all at once, and this should take some pressure off you. From all of the information in this chapter, create your own list of priorities. Naturally, you aren't going to need to add locks to the doors and windows if your little one is no higher than your hip! On the same note, there is no need to go changing all of your lightbulbs unless you know if your child is over or under sensitive to light.

Understanding Autism

Once you have made the changes and start to see the positive differences with your child, it is so important that you share all of this information with other adults in their lives. When everyone is on the same page, it's not just your child who will benefit but also you and your whole family.

Chapter 4: Walk a Mile In Your Autistic Child's Shoes!

Unless you are an autistic parent, walking in their shoes is going to be impossible. Even then, it's incomparable as your symptoms may differ and you have had years of experience living with ASD. We have already discussed how you can push your senses to the extremes to try and get an idea of what your little one might be feeling but there are still other things many parents struggle with when it comes to having an autistic child.

In this chapter, we are going to go through some of these challenges. We are going to look at the world from an autistic child's perspective and discover how we can improve their lives with compassion and understanding. In no way am I suggesting all parent's fall into these traps. You might read some sections and think that it is absolutely awful that a parent may do or say that. You may read a sentence and think gosh, that's me. You are on a massive learning curve and it's perfectly normal to make mistakes. Nobody is here to judge, no parent is perfect and the more open we are, the more we can learn.

How Does An Autistic Child Understand Anxiety?

Social anxiety disorder is an extreme worry caused by a child's concerns of what people may think of them, of being judged or being rejected. They may even feel embarrassed in front of other people. Needless to say, social anxiety disorder has its own spectrum and could range from nerves when trying a new sport or speaking to others. Some children will start to shake, or even experience shortness of breath, while others may express their anxiety by crying or what would seem to be a tantrum.

For an autistic child, social anxiety is quite common, however, children may not match all of the criteria for social anxiety disorder. One thing that many psychologists will agree on is that social anxiety is something that develops over time after repeated struggles with social interaction. It is also more common in older children because they are more aware of their limitations with social interactions. Another contributing factor could be that ASD children find it hard to make friends as they find it difficult to communicate effectively or understand social situations, so they don't have the same exposure to the social environment as other children.

Some ASD children can be extremely anxious and just the thought of speaking in front of someone outside of their home can be traumatic. In this case, social anxiety is so severe that the child is unable to speak in social situations and this can include with their school friends or even family members. You may find that your child speaks at home, even if the speech is limited, but then as soon as granny or grandad come over, they are mute. This would be known as Selective Mutism (SM). It is not uncommon for children to have a diagnosis of ASD and SM.

So, what can you do for your child who is socially anxious? The first thing to do is never belittle the situation, and obviously, this is something that is completely unintentional. I often hear the words "it's only". For example, "It's only granny, you can speak", or "It's only your friends from school at the park". For us, it is only that person who isn't a stranger, for them, it's not something they have control over. Your gentle persuasion may cause them to feel worse about themselves as they aren't able to overcome their anxiety. It goes back to the mantra you have to remind yourself— it's not that they won't, it's that they can't.

When looking to help overcome social anxiety, remember that it must be at the child's pace. Below you will find some things that can help but it should always be without pressure.

- Know what triggers your child's anxiety. Is it a particular location, group of people, or activity? When you know what triggers the stress, you can help prepare your child for these moments. It's not about avoiding them but instead, providing safe ways for them to overcome their fears.

- Use social stories. We mentioned before how social stories can be created by families in order to introduce the child to situations that may cause anxiety. If there is a birthday party coming up, you could create a social story, even using photos of their friends to introduce the activity.

- Prepare a visual timetable. Certain times of the day may cause more stress and anxiety, for example, when one class ends and the next begins, or lunchtimes. A visual timetable helps the child to see what is coming up in their day.

- Introduce relaxation techniques. Deep breathing, visualization and meditation are all excellent techniques that can help ASD children to reduce their anxiety. There are lots of videos on YouTube on guided meditation for autistic children and autism calming sensory videos if you aren't sure where to begin.

- Weighted blankets. Weighted blankets are also known as an autism or sensory blanket.

Yasmin Akhtar

> They are filled with special materials that apply pressure to the body and a sense of security and even relaxation. They can be used during the day to help with meltdowns or for a better night's sleep.

Your speech and language therapist will be able to help you and your child with communication and social anxiety. You can also read a lot more in my next book for families with autistic children.

Beating the Baby Talk

A pet peeve of mine, even before embarking on my career, was baby talk. I'm sure we all have that one family member who comes up to your new-born and in the highest voice pitch ever starts gobbling "cuchy coos" and "ohh look at the birdie" "look at the little woof ". In what world would you go up to Granny, tug on her cheeks and say, "who wants to play with the woof?" We fall into the habit of talking to little people as if they are from another planet, rather than speaking to them like a little person.

For autistic children, the baby talk often continues, even into adulthood. Whether they are spoken to slowly, loudly, or in a tone that only comes across as being spoken down to, it makes ASD children, teenagers and adults feel as if they are stupid. As a parent, you aren't likely to talk to your child the same

54

way you would your partner or a friend, but there is no need to go to the other extreme either.

Again, the baby-talk issue is unlikely to come from you. Misconceptions of autism are what causes others to speak to autistic people differently to others. There is no harm in politely reminding people that your child is autistic and not deaf or stupid. Autistic teenagers might be able to do this themselves, but younger children need you in their corner.

How to Help Your Child Make Friends

Don't punish yourself if the thought of your child having no friends has crossed your mind. There is no way to sugar coat it, your child may struggle to make friends. Nevertheless, this is a problem that is becoming less and less prevalent thanks to autism awareness and inclusion in schools.

In the past, having an autistic child in the classroom would have been considered strange, teachers and carers were not prepared and didn't have the same knowledge and support as they do now. As ASD wasn't properly understood, or as widely diagnosed, exclusion, teasing and even bullying may have occurred.

Watching children interact in a classroom today provides hope for all humanity. Differences are the new normal, so normal in fact that it is hardly an aspect. I have seen children willingly sit next to autistic children and talk away to them as if it were any other classmate. Children don't see a diagnosis. They will notice that their friend is quiet, doesn't like to hold hands or avoids running in the playground, nevertheless, they don't need to label this. But what happens when we step out of the classroom? Adults happen!

It broke my heart to hear one dad tell me a parent didn't want their child sitting next to his because they were autistic. Though rare, there are still some people who are worried about their child 'catching' autism. They aren't worried about autism being contagious, the concern is that their children may pick up on the habits or behaviours of ASD children and start to copy them.

If you are unfortunate enough to experience this, my only advice is to steer well clear of this person. Their concerns for their children may take over their intelligent and logical mind. You may want to explain what autism is, but you may also find yourself getting more upset. In any case, the teacher should have set them straight. That being said, don't punish their child because they don't understand autism. If your child shows an interest in this friend, you can still invite them over for playdates and hope the parents have gained some understanding of autism. Be the better parent! It's about your child making friends, you don't need to be friends with the parents.

Social stories will again be a great resource when helping your child make friends. As long as other parents don't mind, you can take photos of the children together to create your own stories. Another idea is to make sure your child is around children who have the same interests. Look for after school clubs or activities in your area. Your little one will feel more comfortable making friends when there are activities that they love. If any of these situations make them feel uncomfortable or anxious, don't force the matter.

Instead, think about creating your own activity club at home. Let's say your child likes insects. Could you squeeze in an hour a week to invite a few children over who also like insects? You could go on insect hunts, plan colouring activities, read stories or watch videos. Have special insect biscuits!

Use your support network as much as possible. It's not to say that your autistic child can only make friends with other autistic children, but it does help to be around other like-minded parents who are worried about the same things and who are motivated by the same goal. Your speech therapist and school will support your child to learn and establish social skills, but more than anything, keep practicing and know that developing social skills is a continuous effort for long term success.

Believe That Your Autistic Child Loves You

Of course, deep down you know that your child loves you and every inch of your logical brain knows that they may not express their love in the same way as other children because of their difficulties with physical contact, expressing their emotions, or both. Still, the heart isn't as logical, and this can be extremely hard for some parents to overcome.

Children in general are hard work! I always say that it's the best job in the world, but it's also the hardest. Receiving a hug at the end of the day, a smile and an 'I love you' can reassure you, let you know that you are on the right track. Even not being able to make eye contact can be upsetting. You may tell your child that you love them and get no response. The meltdowns in supermarkets even cause you to feel that your child dislikes you. None of these things means your child doesn't love you.

Rather than dwelling on whether your child will ever be able to show you their love, focus on having fun together. Take initiative when it comes to playtime and do the things that they like. Celebrate all of the wins, no matter how small they may be. Your goal

Understanding Autism

should be to create a strong and loving bond with your child, and this will provide you with plenty of enjoyment, love, and reassurance. Above all, never assume that you know what or how your autistic child is feeling.

Seeing the world from your child's perspective is continuous. Each new situation for them will require you to put yourself in their shoes, be aware of existing or new triggers and find ways that will reduce the anxiety in the hope that they can start to enjoy aspects of everyday life. It will require patience and maybe one or more types of therapy. Patience is also a necessity when it comes to your child's therapies. Changes won't occur overnight. This doesn't mean to say that what you do isn't having an effect. It's your consistency and understanding that will allow you to begin to see positive impacts.

Chapter 5: Therapy And Beyond

There are many aspirations and goals when your child starts speech therapy. I won't list them because we are now aware of the differences in symptoms. Just to make sure, a child with selective mutism may not have the same goals as another child who has extreme reactions to touch, and so forth.

When I speak to parents, I tend to hear a general goal from the parent's point of view— and yes, you are allowed to have goals too. It goes without saying that meltdowns have a huge strain on your little one, but we shouldn't ignore the impact that they have on your lives. I don't need to tell you about the fear, not knowing what to do, that crushing feeling when you realize you can't do anything, even the embarrassment of those staring at you.

Everything mentioned previously plus the therapies will hopefully reduce the number and intensity of your child's meltdowns. But we are going to dedicate this chapter to therapies you can do at home that will also help. Before taking a closer look at these therapies, I want to share the advice of some parents who are practicing successful techniques and seeing the differences in meltdowns.

Go back to understanding things from their point of view. Meltdowns may not seem advantageous, but you should remember that your child is expressing emotions. Don't judge them or pretend to understand. Find ways to genuinely empathize.

Show them that they are safe. Talking to your child and trying to explain reason may well fall on deaf ears. Know what makes your child feel safe. It could be a sensory blanket, a particular toy, singing a song, whatever it is that calms your child.

Do not worry about who is watching. It's going to happen; your child will have a meltdown in public and people will not only stare but also judge. This may cause you to feel obliged to punish your child. It may work with any other child, however, for ASD children, it will only cause them to remember this situation as a negative one.

Open up that ASD Mary Poppins bag. Parents get into the habit of packing a bag for all possibilities. Make sure your bag includes those special items that will help them to relax. When adding things to your bag, let your child choose the items they like rather than things you think they need.

After the meltdown, concentrate on coping mechanisms. As much as you want to try and help your child during a meltdown, more often than not, you will have to ride the metaphorical storm. Once the meltdown is over, it's time to look at coping mechanisms such as being in nature, their special place, yoga, or meditation.

Taking it back to the grander picture, there are still certain therapies that you can begin at home, all of which have extensive studies that show their benefits and are risk-free. Your child may begin with some of these therapies, but you can still continue at home. As therapies, you may need to do a little further research, or continue reading this series of books for more guided help.

Time to Play

It doesn't take a qualified psychologist to tell you that floor time is a type of therapy that involves you getting down on the floor so that you can interact with your child at the same level. It's a relationship-based type of therapy that aims to boost interest in the world around them, engage in relationships, develop two-way and complex communication and emotional ideas and thinking. Floor time should be part of your daily routine.

It's important to remember that playtime is child-led, meaning they will choose the activities. Interactions will start off relatively simple and then grow in complexity. Let's say a child is stroking a toy lion. You could stroke a toy elephant. The next step would be to put your elephant next to their lion. This action encourages the child to interact with both the lion and the elephant. Initially this is to support your child to develop 'sharing attention' on the same item/activity. Once your child is comfortable with you sharing the same space/toys then you can add language or stories to help maintain focus and even to develop problem-solving skills. Gradually, the playtime will involve more animals and even the entire ecosystem.

Play Therapy

Play therapy sounds very similar to floor time but it is actually quite different. This is a great type of therapy as for children, it is just playing, but a trained play therapist is able to reveal the underlying insights of the child's play and interactions. Play therapy is a wonderful solution for children who find it difficult to make friends, struggle in social situations, are stressed or anxious or if they are displaying inappropriate behaviours.

Play therapy involves a wide range of toys such as figures, puppets, sand, drawing and painting. How children interact with toy figures can express more about how certain social situations make them feel, drawings can often tell you more about the child's emotions. Unlike floor play, you want to take more of a backseat during play therapy. Sit down with them at their level but the goal is less about interaction and more about understanding what they may otherwise not be able to tell you.

Speech and Language Therapy

Speech therapy is vital for children who display difficulties with language and social communication because it affects and will continue to affect so many other areas of their lives. That being said, it takes rather a lot of knowledge to be able to help your child from home. What you definitely don't want to do is start trying something that may cause confusion. The first thing to do is to have your child assessed for speech and language development. Your speech therapist will then support you and your child's school to set some achievable communication targets that you and the school can work on. Your therapist will discuss and demonstrate techniques with you which you can try at home.

Without wanting to drop it into the conversation too many times, one of my following books is dedicated to speech and language therapy. We will go over everything from speech sounds, tone of voice, understanding spoken language, understanding body language and facial expressions and more. We will look at social stories in detail to help your child improve communication in a variety of social situations. For now, it goes without saying that when you speak to your child, keep your language simple and at the same level as your child's understanding. Keep your speech rate normal, not too fast, or slow. This will help your child to match your communication style which they can then generalize in other situations outside of the home. One of the difficulties children with ASD have is initiating interaction. If this is a skill your child needs to develop, practice this during play activities. First, observe your child and give them a chance to initiate interaction, this might not necessarily be through words. Don't feel you have to talk, in this instance 'silence is good'. This will give your child the opportunity to initiate talking if they want to so don't rush to talk or to keep talking if there is no response from your child. Just be available to respond or extend play or language as your child plays with his toys.

Applied Behaviour Analysis (ABA)

Many parents love this type of therapy because the goal is both measurable and specific. Children also do well at learning new skills. The idea is to take the task you wish to learn and break it down into smaller, more achievable steps. So, if you wanted to teach an older child to make a sandwich, your first step would be to prepare ingredients, step 2 would be to butter the bread, step three to put the butter away and so on.

Yasmin Akhtar

Once you have shown your child how to do the first step, you can practice until they succeed, bearing in mind you may have to show them several times. When they achieve step 1, you offer a ton of praise, genuine excitement and possibly a small reward. Repeat the process with the rest of the steps.

There are lots of online videos and short courses that you can take if you want to gain more confidence in Applied Behaviour Analysis and also ideas on how to break down specific tasks. Nevertheless, it is quite straightforward as long as you are patient.

Relationship Development Intervention (RDI)

RDI takes the focus away from ASD symptoms and focuses on finding the missing elements in order to develop relationships. It relies heavily on the parents' participation as the aim is to change the way the whole family thinks. RDI specialists will work with all family members and it might be something as simple as just learning how to slow down or more complex like balancing the family's schedule.

RDI encourages flexible thinking, the ability to put things in context, problem-solving, learning how to cope with change, and learning more about the emotions of others and controlling behaviour in social situations. As the primary therapist is the parent, it's perfect for the home environment. That being said, before taking on RDI, it is highly recommended that you learn the techniques from a professional.

Parent-Child Interaction Therapy (PCI)

PCI isn't just for autism and has been shown to help children who struggle to communicate and sometimes become aggressive. Aggression can be related to frustrations with not being able to communicate their needs and wants effectively. PCI as the name suggests is therapy geared towards supporting parents to become more aware of their own interaction style. Knowing how you communicate with your child will help you to be better equipped and support your child develop their interaction skills.

There original PCI courses that are available that offer training and offer 12 to 20 sessions. I am not sure if any NHS service offers as many clinic sessions as the course suggests, we have adapted this course in our service to suit our needs, timeframes, and budgets.

As with some of the other therapies, you will need guidance. This guidance is more hands-on. PCI requires quite a few sessions; however, some services offer 4 clinic sessions other may offer more or less.

Yasmin Akhtar

You may be offered this type of therapy, depending on the needs of your child. Usually your therapist will video you playing with your child for about 10-minutes in clinic. You then watch the video together, your therapist will ask you to notice how you are talking to and responding to your child, how you are engaging with your child in play. Are you asking lots of questions when your child does not have any language yet? Are you waiting for your child to initiate interaction, using eye contact/sounds/words/signs or are you talking, and your child is playing? You can then decide on one or 2 things you want to work on until your next appointment a week later. Don't worry, your therapist will support you to look for things in the video, they will explain and demonstrate strategies on how you can improve your own interaction skills.

I always start my sessions by reassuring parents, that I am not here to judge them but rather to support them as much as possible so that they can help their child. While watching their video back, I have so many parents saying "oh, I did not know I did that", the video can be very empowering as it will show you the skills you need to work on and adapt when you are interacting with your child. It is not always about things you have to improve, there are always positives where we will reassure you that you are doing great!

Understanding Autism

The strategies you learn can help with meltdowns, increasing attention and listening, taking turns, and improving social behaviours. Above all, this type of therapy can help to reduce your frustration when things aren't going as you had hoped.

It's true that many parents are already busy juggling a mountain of responsibilities and taking on courses might not be a possibility. The internet is a great resource for finding more information on these therapies and you should definitely talk to your health visitor, speech therapist or a paediatrician or team for resources and practical ideas. On that note, our final chapter will be about where to find further help and about taking care of yourself.

Chapter 6: The importance of Self-Care and Asking For Help for Parents With ASD Children

Parents will often fall into the habit of not asking for help. As a mother, I felt that motherhood was natural and as so many women seem to bring up their children effortlessly, I must be doing something wrong. The truth is, we all need some help, and this is not a sign of weakness. Your situation may be unique, but the one thing that parents of children with autism have in common is the need to create a support network.

You might feel a bit shy about this but remember, if you don't ask, you won't get it. The good news is that there is so much support nowadays it's just finding the right way to reach out. From the point of view of a speech therapist, we are here to provide therapies and strategies to help your child's communication development and interaction skills. But we are also here for you. We have the knowledge and an amazing listening ear to help you get the solutions and resources that you need. So, the first step to getting help is to ask your team of highly qualified experts. This might be with additional help for your child or support for you.

Specialist Support for Siblings of children with ASD

Sibs- If you have other children, you will probably find that having an autistic sibling can take its toll. Your other children may struggle to understand why your autistic child gets so much attention. They may act out or find other ways to get your attention. You may find it hard to explain autism to siblings. Sibs is an organization dedicated to those who have a disabled brother or sister and while I don't consider ASD a disability, there is still a massive amount of support for siblings.

Beat Autism- Beat Autism was founded by parents of a child with Asperger Syndrome and a second child with severe classic autism. The site has learning groups, a special area dedicated to dads and some very handy information about disability and living allowance that may help you with financial difficulties.

Let's take a look at some specific areas that, when handled in the right way, can allow you to feel more relaxed and less "it's me and my child against the world".

Yasmin Akhtar

Getting Rid Of The Social Stigma of Having an Autistic Child

It doesn't have to be a meltdown that causes others to stare at you and your child. If your child starts rocking or spinning or perhaps continuously talks about their interest without gauging the social situation, people may start to look at both of you as if you have just been dropped off from another planet. You might notice that even friends start treating you differently, looks of pity or walking around on eggshells. I have heard of family members saying things like "How is he today?" like it's a bout of the flu.

When it comes to friends and family, it's often a good idea to wait until you have a diagnosis, and you know about the therapies. You will find that when you are more confident with your own knowledge, it will become easier to explain. Encourage them to ask questions and speak openly about autism rather than treat it as a taboo subject. Open conversations help you to all be on the same page, which will benefit the whole family later on.

The stigma behind autism is changing. Some organizations are even working to change the name from Autism Spectrum Disorder to Autism Spectrum Condition. It might not seem like a huge step but it's still a step further away from disability— which in turn has an effect on the way society views autism.

While you can make a difference with how friends and family treat you as a parent of an autistic child, society is a little harder to control. If your child is having a meltdown and others stare, turn away. It's easier said than done but it's better to physically turn your attention to your child than to explain your personal situation to strangers. Nevertheless, I am a firm believer in putting a smile on my face and politely correcting anyone who makes an inaccurate comment, or any statement that hurts your feelings. Be proud to defend the world of autism.

How To Manage Advice Overload from Well-Meaning People

To a great extent, this is also related to how others view autism, or at least their lack of understanding. The absolute worst case is when your child is going through a meltdown and somebody says, "If I were you...". They might witness this particular moment, but they aren't living it day in and day out. The temptation to snap may consume you. The only problem is, it's more than likely that you will feel bad later and they will label you as the crazy parent.

Deep breathing and counting to ten are often enough for you to compose your thoughts and respond in the right way. "Thank you for your advice but it may not apply to my child" is often enough and better for your personal self-esteem than faking an "Oh yes, I hadn't thought of that".

As with the stigma that surrounds autism, don't stand for rudeness or insults. Your focus has to remain on your child but once they are in an emotional and mental safe place highlight the lack of understanding and poor behaviour.

The Right Amount of Research Without Research Overload

The internet has the answer to almost all of our questions. You will find scientific studies, research in progress, articles and blogs from professionals and forums with questions and advice from other parents. It can become a little bit addictive. Some people get sucked into the world of social media; I can spend ages looking at houses. I'm sure we all have an internet vice.

Be careful that you don't get so sucked in that you are spending too much time on research rather than putting your learning into practice. Only you will know how much time is too much but if you feel like you are a little too addicted to the research, write a list of questions you want to find the answer to and try not to stray off the topic. Set a timer if necessary.

Understanding Autism

You could also limit your research sessions to a certain number of questions. Keep of note of those other questions for later on. There is an awful lot to take in, your brain might appreciate bite-sized information.

Me Time! Finding Time for Yourself—No! This Is Not Selfish

This is one of the key times when asking for help if crucial. Before becoming a spouse, you were a free and single person, before becoming a parent, you were a spouse, you can't forget either of these two people. It might seem selfish, but you still need to be able to enjoy a night with your friends, a shopping trip alone or a weekly gym/yoga session. If you are in a relationship, some form of date night should be celebrated. Many couples struggle to keep the romance alive when their entire focus becomes their autistic child.

You need time for yourself because this gives you time to work on and improve your mental and physical well-being. How can you expect to take care of your little one and your family if you are not well? Make sure you give your partner time and space to look after themselves and vice versa. Initially, you will find it hard to leave your child with someone else so that you can enjoy the luxury of a date night. At some point, you just have to bite the bullet. Start off

75

Yasmin Akhtar

with just 30 minutes, a walk together, maybe something close to home. Once you know everything is ok, you can start taking a little bit longer for yourselves. I always advise couples to ban the word autism from their very rare time alone. It's not awful and it's not burying your head in the sand, it's time for you.

Until you are able to leave your child with someone else, it's time to get creative with your time. Mornings can be ideal for getting things done while children are still asleep. Instead of a romantic dinner, why not a romantic breakfast. If you can't get to the gym, look for exercise videos online and start the day with a boost of energy.

Even sitting in the garden with a cup of coffee for 5 minutes can change your perspective. No devices, no noise, just take in the world. Reflect on the good things in life and know that things will all fall into place.

Having Faith in Your Parenting Skills

I remember a mum telling me once that after the diagnosis, she felt that her child had no future. For her, this felt like a loss that needed to be grieved, both for the mum and the child. This was to be their fate. It's not true that your child doesn't have a future, it is true that their future may be different but there are

76

numerous stories of ASD children who go on to lead fruitful lives. The only thing that you can be sure of is that you will do your best.

In the first few months of parenthood, you may feel like you have no idea what you're doing, you may be waiting for that moment when the natural instincts kick in. In reality, there is no one moment when it literally kicks in, we just start to feel more comfortable in this new role. By toddler stage, you are in full swing, you know when they are going to fall, what food they are going to leave on their plate, which toy they will turn to for comfort. A diagnosis might feel like your instincts are pulled out from underneath you. Try to see this moment as a little shake-up of your instincts but they are still there. Nobody knows your child better than you. Nobody loves them more than you and although therapists are going to provide amazing techniques and strategies, nobody is going to help your child as much as you are.

When you are sitting down with that coffee for 5 minutes, remind yourself that you are a good parent and that even if mistakes are made, you are doing your best and you are a good parent.

Conclusion

In our first step to understanding ASD, we have looked at some of the most common symptoms. You might feel like some of the symptoms you see in your child clearly relate and others don't present. ASD is literally that, a very wide spectrum. To walk a mile in your little one's steps, you have to understand that each child will be wearing a very different shoe.

Looking back at the history of ASD has given us a chance to see just how far scientific studies have come and our knowledge of this condition. We have gone from seeing autism as a mental disability to seeing it as a manageable set of symptoms that can lead to a perfectly normal life. Not only this, but we are seeing more and more cases of autistic children growing up to become highly successful adults. Just look at the American Idol contestant James Durbin, or Tim Burton, the movie director.

Diagnosing ASD is a long and difficult process, one where a team of specialists work together by using various tools and assessments. Don't be scared to ask your team any question, big or small. Trust me, no doubt is too insignificant. Take on board all of the information you are given but give yourself time to process before jumping into action.

Understanding Autism

We now know that autistic children struggle with changes in routine. In my heart, I really hope you are motivated to try the tips and strategies that we have looked at. Ironically, at the same time, I have to urge you not to rush into too many changes at once. Definitely create a plan of the ideas you would like to introduce and find a way that works within your family dynamics. As you have probably already begun baby proofing and toddler proofing your home and considering safety is the most important, I recommend you start here.

Unfortunately, there is little we can do about the busy-bodies in the world who stare when you are trying to cope with a meltdown. You are going to come across people who talk down to your child or talk over them as if they don't understand what is being said. Keep that big smile on your face and don't feel bad about educating them. More often than not, these people mean no harm, they just aren't all that skilled at tact and diplomacy and they don't understand.

This is another reason why it is important to take care of yourself. Aside from needing the energy to look after your autistic child and face all of the other responsibilities you have, a healthier happier you will be more able to handle the social stigma that surrounds autism. I know I sound like a broken record but taking a little bit of time to yourself is not selfish, it's a necessity.

On a similar note, I want to take a minute to send you a virtual hug. Yes, it sounds cheesy, but I want you to remember that you are an amazing parent who is doing an amazing job at raising an amazing child. Don't let anyone tell you otherwise or make you feel like you are not awesome. Parents of autistic children go beyond awesome. Mistakes are not a weakness or a sign that you are doing everything wrong. They are learning opportunities that everyone in the world is entitled to make. Never punish yourself or be too hard on yourself.

You might be coming to the end of this book and still have questions or concerns. Remember at the beginning of the book I said that this is the first stage, learning what to expect and making some small changes to see bigger results. Information overload is a real thing and I firmly believe that with so much information on ASD and limited time to read, it makes more sense to break down autism into easily digestible books.

The next book in this series is going to focus more on the daily activities your child may face. We know that hygiene can be challenging for those with sensory problems. Brushing hair and teeth, bath time and getting dressed are milestones for all toddlers, but it can be harder for autistic children to master these skills. If you are looking for more information on things like potty training, hand washing, and even taking medicine, I hope you will look out for my next book.

I would like to thank you for reading this book. I hope you found the information useful. I am always looking for constructive feedback and I would love to hear about things you would find helpful.

I will be extremely grateful, if you could leave a quick review on Amazon for me, I can take note of your feedback and add to the series of ASD books. Good luck and I look forward to hearing your success stories.

References

Ansel, K. (2020, June 22). *Autism Spectrum
Disorders (ASD) and Diet*. EatRight.
https://www.eatright.org/health/diseases-
and-conditions/autism/nutrition-for-your-
child-with-autism-spectrum-disorder-asd

Applied Behavioral Analysis. (2017, December
1). *How is ADOS (Autism Diagnostic
Observation Schedule) Used to Identify
ASD?* Applied Behavioral Analysis | How
to Become an Applied Behavior Analyst.
https://www.appliedbehavioranalysisedu.o
rg/how-is-ados-autism-diagnostic-
observation-schedule-used-to-identify-
asd/#:%7E:text=ADOS%20stands%20for

%20Autism%20Diagnostic,available%20i

n%2015%20different%20languages

Autism: Types of Autism Spectrum Disorders.

(n.d.). DHSS Alaska Gov.

http://dhss.alaska.gov/dph/wcfh/Pages/auti

sm/spectrum.aspx

British Medical Association. (2020, September 7).

Autism spectrum disorder. The British

Medical Association Is the Trade Union

and Professional Body for Doctors in the

UK. https://www.bma.org.uk/what-we-

do/population-health/child-health/autism-

spectrum-disorder

Floortime. (n.d.). Autism Speaks.

https://www.autismspeaks.org/floortime-0

Yasmin Akhtar

Mandal, A. (2019, February 26). *Autism History*. News-Medical.Net. https://www.news-medical.net/health/Autism-History.aspx

National Autistic Society. (n.d.-a). *Diagnostic tools - a guide for all audiences*. https://www.autism.org.uk/advice-and-guidance/topics/diagnosis/diagnostic-tools/all-audiences

National Autistic Society. (n.d.-b). *Sensory differences - a guide for all audiences*. https://www.autism.org.uk/advice-and-guidance/topics/sensory-differences/sensory-differences/all-audiences

Understanding Autism

National Institute of Mental Health. (2020a, April 2). *NIMH » Autism Spectrum Disorder (ASD)*. NIMH.NIH. https://www.nimh.nih.gov/health/statistics/autism-spectrum-disorder-asd.shtml

National Institute of Mental Health. (2020b, April 2). *NIMH » Autism Spectrum Disorder (ASD)*. NIMH.NIH. https://www.nimh.nih.gov/health/statistics/autism-spectrum-disorder-asd.shtml

NHS website. (2019, July 12). *Signs of autism in adults*. Nhs.Uk. https://www.nhs.uk/conditions/autism/signs/adults/

Yasmin Akhtar

Oughtisms, A. A. (2011, July 25). *"I'll call a kid a zebra…": Recognising "Fashionable Autism."* Autism & Oughtisms. https://autismandoughtisms.wordpress.com/2011/07/22/ill-call-a-kid-a-zebra-recognising-fashionable-autism/

Pallardy, R. (n.d.). *Donald Triplett | American autism patient*. Encyclopedia Britannica. https://www.britannica.com/biography/Donald-Triplett

PCIT International. (n.d.). *What is PCIT?* PCIT. http://www.pcit.org/what-is-pcit.html

Pearson Assessment. (n.d.). *Autism Diagnostic Interview, Revised (ADI-R)*. https://www.pearsonclinical.co.uk/Psychol

ogy/ChildMentalHealth/ChildMentalHealt

h/AutismDiagnosticInterviewRevised(ADI

-

R)/AutismDiagnosticInterviewRevised(A

DI-R).aspx

Play2Change. (n.d.). Play2change.

https://www.play2change.co.uk

Rudy, L. (2020, September 3). *6 Easy, Lower-*

Cost Ways to Become Your Child's autism

Therapist. Verywell Health.

https://www.verywellhealth.com/low-cost-

autism-therapies-parents-can-provide-at-

home-4172365